# At the ZOO

# INTRODUCTION

There are well over a hundred zoological parks, sea life centres and animal parks across the United Kingdom. They house thousands of different animal species from all over the world. From birds to reptiles, big cats to marsupials and fish to insects, there is a huge selection of creatures to see. Some zoos are very big and take the whole day to explore. Even then, you may have to return to see all the animals, especially if some only come out at night. Other zoos and parks can be very small with just a few animals on show. Often, it is these little zoos that allow you to get close to and meet some of the animals. No matter which park you visit you'll need to be patient and quiet as many animals are shy or timid.

Modern zoos try their best to give animals as much space as possible. They also try to mimic their natural home, or habitat, so the animals can live happy lives. Many zoos have creatures that are in danger in the wild because of hunting or because their habitats are being destroyed. These zoos play an important role in making sure these species survive.

We've selected a wide variety of animals in this book that you can search for when you visit a zoo. Some can only be found in one or two specific zoos whereas others are common sights in most zoos you might visit. Those that occur in fewer zoos usually carry a higher i-SPY score because they are more difficult for you to spot.

## How to use your i-SPY book

The animals in the book are arranged in groups starting with the different types of mammals (including big cats, primates and marsupials), then continuing through birds, fish, amphibians and other aquatic creatures, reptiles, spiders, insects and other invertebrates. You need 1000 points to send off for your i-SPY certificate (see page 64) but that is not too difficult because there are masses of points in every book. Each entry has a star or circle and points value beside it. The stars represent harder to spot entries. As you make each i-SPY, write your score in the circle or star. There are questions dotted throughout the book that can increase your i-SPY score. Check your answers on page 63.

**TIGER**

**Points: 15**

Tigers are easy animals to recognize. They have orange, black and white stripes on their fur and Siberian tigers can reach over 3 metres (10 feet) long. Tigers live on their own for most of the time in forests and grasslands. Sadly, the number of tigers left in the wild continues to go down every year.

### WHITE TIGER

**Points: 25**

White tigers are Bengal tigers that have a gene that changes their fur to white instead of orange. However, they still have the same stripes as normal tigers. Also, all white tigers have blue eyes.

 **Points: 20**

### JAGUAR

These big cats live in South America and have black spots shaped like roses. Young jaguars stay with their mothers for two years or longer so they can learn to hunt. Jaguars are unlike many other cats as they do not avoid water and can swim very well. This cub is only a few months old.

### CHEETAH

**Points: 15**

Cheetahs live in eastern and southwestern Africa and are the fastest land mammals in the world. They can accelerate faster than most cars. Their tan coats with black spots help them blend into the dry grasslands where they live.

15  **Points: 15**

Most leopards are light in colour with distinctive black spots. They are much bigger, heavier and stronger than cheetahs and jaguars. Leopards like to spend their time up in trees.

**LION**

Points: 10

These are the only big cats that live in groups or 'prides' as they are known. They are sometimes referred to as the King of the Beasts! Male lions have shaggy manes and are bigger than females. African lions have a slightly different appearance to Asiatic lions with the Asiatic male having a smaller mane and a bigger tail tassel than its African counterpart.

**Points: 20**

### GELADA BABOON

Gelada baboons live in big groups of up to 600 members. They separate into smaller groups to look for food during the day. The mountain grasslands of Ethiopia are home to them.

### SULAWESI MACAQUE

**Points: 10**
double with answer

Intelligent and social, these monkeys form close relationships with other members of their group. They communicate by grunting and will often smack their lips to greet one another.

*Why do adult males yawn?*

**Points: 5**

### COTTON-TOP TAMARIN MONKEY

Cotton-top tamarin monkeys are easily recognized in the rainforest because of the fan of long, white hair on their heads. They have black faces, grey-brown backs and white underbellies.

## WHITE-HANDED GIBBON

**Points: 30**

Also known as lar gibbons, they have long arms and hook-shaped hands to help them swing through the rainforest. They can move through the forest at over 50 km/h (30 mph) and bridge gaps as wide as 15 metres (50 feet).

 **Points: 5**

## WHITE-FACED SAKI MONKEY

Males and females look quite different from each other. The males are easiest to recognize as they have jet black hair on their bodies with whitish faces and black noses. Females are grey-brown in colour with a fringed hairline.

## COMMON MARMOSET

**Points: 10**

These very cute grey-faced monkeys have large white tufts of fur on the sides of their heads and a white patch above their eyes. They have claws on their fingers which help them hold on to the bark of the trees they like to climb.

**Points: 5**

### GOELDI'S MONKEY

These little monkeys have black hair all over their bodies and live in the Amazon rainforest. They eat fruit and insects and, unlike many other monkeys, spend a lot of time on the ground.

### HOWLER MONKEY

**Points: 25**

True to their name, these residents of Central and South America can be heard up to 5 km (3 miles) away when the whole group starts howling at top volume. They have beards, long tails and thick hair that can be red, brown or black. This one is a juvenile.

### SPIDER MONKEY

Points: 15

15

They live in the tropical forests of Central and South America from Mexico all the way to Brazil. They get their name because their arms are just as long as their legs and they have very long tails. When threatened they make a noise that sounds like barking.

5

Points: 5

### RING-TAILED LEMUR

As their name suggests, to spot one of these you just need to look at their distinctive black and white ringed tails. They have bright orange eyes, black noses and white tufted ears. In the wild, the live on the island of Madagascar.

**Points: 20**
double with answer

ORANGUTAN

Orangutan means 'person of the forest' and it's not difficult to see why these primates have been given this name. They are close relatives of humans and extremely clever animals. Orangutans are found only in Borneo and Sumatra but sadly their habitat is being destroyed.

*In the forest, do orangutans spend most of their time on the ground or in trees?*

### WESTERN LOWLAND GORILLA

**Points: 15**

Although slightly smaller than mountain gorillas these great apes are still formidable beasts. The dominant male in a group is often referred to as a 'silverback' due to the grey hair that grows on its back. If threatened, these males will stand upright, pound their chests and roar. Sometimes they will charge or throw things.

**Points: 15**

### CHIMPANZEE

Often called chimps, they live in large, mixed male and female groups in the jungles of Africa. The dominant male is called the alpha male and each individual in the group knows its place. Chimps are very intelligent and can make tools to help them get food.

### Points: 30

**TENREC**

These little mammals are found in Madagascar and other parts of Africa. They look a bit like a mix between hedgehogs, mice and shrews. They are omnivores but mainly eat insects.

**CHIPMUNK**

### Points: 30

Probably the cutest of the squirrel family, these little rodents are found throughout North America and Eurasia. They hibernate but don't store fat to live off. Instead, they nibble away at the food that they have collected during the summer.

### Points: 20
double with answer

**SKUNK**

Known for their smelly defensive spray, these black and white furry mammals are omnivores. They have a varied diet that consists of eggs, reptiles, insects, plants, fruit, small mammals and even fish.

*When do they look for food?*

### MARMOT

**Points: 20**

Most species of marmot are found in mountainous regions. They are quite large and live in self-dug burrows or rock piles. Animals, such as wolves, hunt them so marmots let out a loud whistle to warn others if a predator is spotted.

**Points: 10**

### CHINCHILLA

These rodents are from the Andes in South America. They live high up in the mountains in colonies called 'herds'. They are thought to have the softest fur of all land mammals.

### DIK DIK

**Points: 20**

Dik diks are very small antelopes that live on the African plains. They have large ears and large eyes and can grab things with their noses. Dik diks get their name from the noise they make when they are frightened.

**Points: 25**

## ROCK HYRAX

Amazingly, the closest living relative of the little rock hyrax is the elephant. They look a bit like guinea pigs with their short ears and tails, but are much bigger than them. They have long black whiskers on their muzzles and live in rock crevices.

## AYE-AYE

**Points: 25**

With their wide-eyed expression, big ears and oversized tail, it's difficult not to find this little nocturnal lemur anything but adorable. They live in the rainforests of Madagascar and spend most of their lives trying to avoid going down to the forest floor.

### RACCOON

**Points: 15**

These animals are a familiar sight in North America and can be found in marshland, forests, prairies and even towns and cities. This is because they have a varied diet and are not particularly fussy about what they eat. They have grey coats, black and white faces and nimble front paws.

**Points: 5**

### FERRET

Female ferrets are called 'jills' and a group of ferrets is called a 'business'. Ferrets are the domesticated form of the European polecat and have short legs and long, slender bodies. Wild polecats hunt at night for rabbits, birds and rodents.

### RED SQUIRREL

**Points: 15**

Red squirrels are native to Britain and Europe, where they live in deciduous and coniferous woodland. They spend most of their time looking for nuts, seeds and berries. They are much smaller than their North American cousin, the grey squirrel.

Points: 10

## EURASIAN OTTER

These semi-aquatic mammals are long and slender with distinctive brown fur on top and white fur below. They mainly eat fish although they supplement their diet with insects, birds and amphibians.

## RED PANDA

Points: 10

These pandas from eastern Asia are tiny in comparison to giant pandas. They have red fur with white snouts, black noses and white-tipped ears. They use their bushy ringed tails to snuggle into. This helps keep them warm during cold nights in their mountain homes.

## PINE MARTEN

Points: 20

Similar in size to domestic cats, pine martens have brown fur and yellow or cream throats. During the cold winter months this fur grows longer to keep them warm. They have semi-retractable claws which allow them to run up and down trees.

**Points: 10**

**MARA**

Maras have long ears and long legs and look like oversize rabbits mixed with guinea pigs. They live in the Pampas grasslands in Argentina, eating mainly grass and sometimes fruit.

**PRAIRIE DOG**

**Points: 10**

The World Wildlife Fund reckons these little chubby-looking mammals from America support over 135 other species due to their habits. For example, they live in underground colonies called 'prairie dog towns' and many other animals use these tunnels for shelter.

**Points: 5**

**GUINEA PIG**

Many people keep guinea pigs as pets. Despite their name, they are not related to pigs nor are they from Guinea. They originally came from the Andes mountains but, apart from those that have escaped from captivity, they no longer live in the wild.

### MEERKAT

**Points: 5**

Meerkats live in large groups and often stand up on their rear legs to gaze into the distance. They work as a team and at any one time, a few individuals will act as lookouts, watching for birds of prey circling above.

 **Points: 20**

### FRUIT BAT

Fruit bats live in Asia, Africa, Australia and the Middle East and don't really look like most other bats. They are often called 'flying foxes' and a close look at their faces will explain why.

### PORCUPINE

**Points: 20**
double with answer

Porcupines may look rather cute but they have needle-like quills and are not to be messed with. Normally, the quills are flat but when porcupines feel threatened they raise their quills for protection.

*Do they have hundreds, thousands or millions of quills?*

## Points: 40   Top Spot!

### BABIRUSA

One of the oddest looking animals you will find in a zoo, the babirusa is a member of the pig family. The male babirusas have strange looking tusks that are actually their upper canine teeth. Although they may not look it, babirusas are very clever animals.

### VISAYAN WARTY PIG

### Points: 15

These pigs are found only in the Philippines and are in danger of becoming extinct in the wild. This is because farmers are clearing most of their habitat. They usually live in groups of up to six and get their name because of the fleshy 'warts' around their face.

### Points: 15

### WILD BOAR

Wild boar are native to the forests of Europe, northwest Africa and Asia. These wild pigs are very stocky and have thick double coats. Their undercoats are soft but their outer coats are hard and bristly.

## WARTHOG

**Points: 10**

Although warthogs look quite ferocious, with their strange looking tusks and snouts, they are actually grazers. They use their snouts to dig for bulbs and roots in the grasslands of Africa where they live.

**Points: 10**

## RED RIVER HOG

As suggested by their name these wild pigs have a striking coat of red hair. They have black legs and a white tuft running down the length of their backs. In the wild, their biggest enemy is the leopard who often hunts them.

**Points: 15**

**TWO-TOED SLOTH**

No mammal is slower than the two-toed sloth and its relative the three-toed sloth. They spend their lives in the treetops of Central and South America and are perfectly adapted for this. Their long claws give them a powerful grip and they can hang upside down for many hours.

**CAPYBARA**

**Points: 10**
double with answer

Capybaras are the world's largest rodents. They are from South America and look like giant guinea pigs. They grow to over 1.3 metres (4 feet) long and can weigh 80 kg (175 pounds).

*Why do their teeth keep growing throughout their lives?*

**Points: 40**  **Top Spot!**

**ARMADILLO**

In Spanish, the armadillo's name means 'little armoured one'. While some species are indeed quite small, giant armadillos can grow to about 1.5 metres (5 feet) long. Their armour is made up of plates which overlap each other.

## AARDVARK

**Points: 20**

These are very odd looking creatures and seem to have the snout from a pig, ears from a rabbit and a tail from a kangaroo. They live in sub-Saharan Africa and forage at night for termites which is their favourite food.

 **Points: 20**

## GIANT ANTEATER

They are giant and they do eat ants – and termites! They rip open anthills and termite mounds with their sharp claws. Their pointed snouts and long tongues help them eat over 30,000 ants and termites every day.

## Points: 10

**ALPACA**

From South America, alpacas are similar to llamas but much smaller. They are known for their soft wool which is very expensive to buy.

**PYGMY GOAT**

## Points: 10

Pygmy goats are originally from West Africa. They are friendly and intelligent little animals and eat mostly grass in the wild. For their size, they produce a lot of milk.

## Points: 15

**EASTERN BONGO**

These animals are now extremely rare in the wild. One reason is because they have been hunted for their beautiful chestnut red coats with white vertical stripes. Males are bigger than females and have longer spiral-shaped horns which can be up to 1 metre (3 feet) long.

## SOUTH AMERICAN TAPIR

**Points: 10**

These animals may look like pigs with short trunks but they are in fact related to rhinoceroses and horses. The trunk is actually a long nose and upper lip. In the forests of Amazonia they use this to strip leaves and find fruits to eat.

 **Points: 40**  **Top Spot!**

## LOWLAND ANOA

They are like small versions of water buffalo and live in the rainforests of Indonesia. Their horns are quite small and point backwards. They sometimes have white markings on their legs and back or under their eyes.

**Points: 30**

### AFRICAN HUNTING DOG

Also known as African painted dogs these fearsome animals roam the open plains and sparse woodlands of sub-Saharan Africa. They are pack animals and have a mottled coat with patches of white, yellow, black and red fur.

### MALAYAN SUN BEAR

**Points: 40**   **Top Spot!**

One of the smallest types of bear, the Malayan sun bear's name comes from the orange markings on its chest. Many people think these markings look like a rising sun. Although smaller than other kinds of bear, they have very powerful jaws and large claws.

**Points: 20**

### GREY WOLF

Also known as the timber or white wolf, this animal develops close relationships and strong social bonds with other members of its pack. Grey wolves can cover great distances and maintain large territories to ensure a steady supply of prey animals.

## GIANT RIVER OTTER

**Points: 30**
double with answer

The giant river otter is the world's largest otter and can sometimes reach 1.8 metres (6 feet) in length. Giant river otters have ears and nostrils that close while they are in the water, webbed feet and water-repellent fur.

*Which large river in South America do these otters live in?*

**Points: 40**   Top Spot!

## WOLVERINE

Although they look like little bears, wolverines are actually related to weasels. They have heavy fur and mainly prey on rodents and rabbits. They live in coniferous forests and cover long distances to find their food.

**Points: 25**

## ONAGER

Related to the donkey, they are very fast runners and belong to a group of animals that includes horses and zebras. Onagers are reddish-brown or yellowish-brown in colour and have a dark stripe down the middle of their back. They usually have white bellies, buttocks and muzzles.

## CONGO BUFFALO

**Points: 25**

These are normally brown or reddish-brown in colour with short coarse hair. Their large drooping ears provide them with excellent hearing. When they need to, they can run at an amazing 40 km/h (25 mph).

 **Points: 10**

## FALLOW DEER

Fallow deer have coats that can be brown, red, black or even pure white in colour. They have white spots on their back during the summer months but their coats usually become darker through the winter.

### DONKEY

**Points: 10**

These belong to the same family as horses and zebras but are much stockier and have long, floppy ears. Wild donkeys are also called asses or burros.

**Points: 15**

### GIRAFFE

These are the tallest animals on Earth and live in Africa. They have extremely long necks to help them reach the highest branches. This means they can eat leaves, fruits and flowers that other herbivores cannot get to.

### OKAPI

**Points: 15**

Although they look a bit like zebras they are actually related to giraffes. They have black and white striped front legs and hindquarters. If you look closely though, their heads and ears are a similar shape to those of giraffes.

**Points: 15**

## ROAN ANTELOPE

Roan antelopes have long white stripes beside their eyes and live in herds of up to 35 individuals, though there is only one adult male in a group. This male fiercely defends the females and younger members of the group against his rivals.

## SCIMITAR-HORNED ORYX

**Points: 15**

Oryx are grazing animals that live in arid parts of Africa. They also live in the Arabian Peninsula but their numbers are very low there. They have long horns that curve up and backwards. Scimitar-horned oryx have pale creamy-coloured bodies with reddish-brown necks and faces.

### BACTRIAN CAMEL

**Points: 5**

Unlike their relatives from Arabia, these camels have two humps. The humps store fat which can be converted to water and energy when needed. This means they can endure long periods of travel even in the harshest of conditions in the desert.

**Points: 5**

### ZEBRA

The zebra has very distinctive black and white stripes and is probably one of the most easily recognized animals on Earth. They are social animals and spend time in herds, grazing together mainly on grass.

### LESSER KUDU

**Points: 15**

Similar to the greater kudu, these handsome antelopes have brown coats with white stripes. The males have long, spiral horns and females occasionally have small ones. These horns are used as musical instruments by local people in Africa.

**Points: 20**

### WHITE RHINOCEROS

Almost all the white rhinos in the wild can be found in only four countries: Kenya, Zimbabwe, South Africa and Namibia. With their huge bulk and two distinctive horns these mammals look as though they belong with the dinosaurs. White rhinos have a square upper lip while black rhinos have a pointed upper lip.

### GREATER ONE-HORNED RHINOCEROS

**Points: 25**

The largest rhinoceros in the world, the greater one-horned rhino lives in Nepal and northern India. It has a single horn about 20-60 cm (8-25 inches) long and a thick grey hide with skin folds. These folds make this rhinoceros look like it is armour-plated.

## HIPPOPOTAMUS

**Points: 15**

In Ancient Greek their name means 'river horse'. So it is not surprising to find that they spend their days submerged in Africa's lakes and rivers. Score points for either the large hippo or the smaller pygmy hippo.

**Points: 15**

## ELEPHANT

These mammals live in herds and are the largest land animals in the world. Males grow long ivory tusks to fight other males with. Elephants flap their large ears to keep cool.

*What are the most obvious differences between African and Indian elephants?*

34

Points: 40    Top Spot!

**POLAR BEAR**

These large bears live in the Arctic, one of the coldest places on Earth. On the sea ice they mainly hunt for seals and are camouflaged by their white coats. However, their fur is not white – it is actually transparent and just appears to be white.

## GIANT PANDA

**Points: 50**   Top Spot!

Everyone has a soft spot for the biggest teddy-bear in the world! Their black and white bodies make them the easiest bear to recognize. To keep their weight up they will eat as much as 12 kg (26 pounds) of bamboo every day.

 **Points: 25**

## EUROPEAN BROWN BEAR

This bear is a relative of the American grizzly bear and was once very common throughout Europe. Although large and heavy, it can run as fast as a racehorse. These bears eat fish during the summer spawning season as well as small animals, nuts, berries, leaves and roots.

**Points: 20**

### STELLER SEA LION

With their big appetites, these mammals are the largest sea lions in the world. They can grow to well over 2.5 metres (8 feet) and live close to the coastlines across the northern Pacific Ocean. They eat octopus, squid and fish.

### SOUTH AMERICAN FUR SEAL

**Points: 15**

South American fur seals have great eyesight and acute hearing. Like other mammals they breathe air but they spend long periods at sea catching krill, sea birds and fish. There are several species of fur seal across the world.

## RED KANGAROO

**Points: 20**

Red kangaroos are the largest marsupials in the world. Marsupial animals look after and suckle their young in pouches on their bellies. From Australia, red kangaroos have powerful legs and can jump almost three times their own height.

**Points: 10**

## RED-NECKED WALLABY

Wallabies are members of the kangaroo family but are usually smaller than their kangaroo cousins. The red-necked wallaby comes from the southeast coast of Australia and Tasmania.

Points: 40    Top Spot!

KOALA

Although they are often called koala bears, they are marsupials and not bears at all. Native to Australia, they lead very inactive lives, spending much of their time asleep in eucalyptus trees.

This is handy, for when they wake up, it's the eucalyptus leaves they feed on. Although it looks as soft as rabbit fur, koala fur is much rougher and feels more like wool to touch.

## SUN CONURE

**Points: 25**

Sun conures are one of the most brightly coloured parrots. They look like they are blushing because of their red cheeks. All parrots have curved beaks and four toes on each foot. Two of these point forward and two point backwards.

**Points: 40** **Top Spot!**

## BLUE-EYED COCKATOO

A native of parts of eastern Papua New Guinea and a few other islands in this region, not much is really known about this tropical bird. It has bright blue skin around its eyes, white plumage and a large yellow crest of feathers on its head.

## BLUE-BELLIED ROLLER

**Points: 20**

These beautiful birds get their names from their colourful stomachs. They live in wooded grasslands and on the edges of forests in central Africa.

**Points: 25**

## BALI STARLING

The plumage of these songbirds is almost entirely white. Bali starlings have long, drooping crests, black wing-tips and tail tips. They have a distinctive blue patch of bare skin around their eyes.

## RAINBOW LORIKEET

**Points: 15**

Male and female rainbow lorikeets look similar to each other. These parrots have green and yellow plumage on their bodies, purple heads, red beaks and red chests.

**Points: 5**

## HYACINTH MACAW

The largest bird in the parrot family, hyacinth macaws have vivid blue feathers and large nut-cracking black beaks. Their orange markings near their beaks and around their eyes make them quite easy to recognize in the Amazon rainforest.

## BLACK STORK

**Points: 20**

Black storks are easy to spot in the zoo becaue of their long red beaks and red legs. In the wild though, despite being quite large, they lead very private lives so can be difficult to find.

**Points: 20**

## GREY-CROWNED CRANE

At a metre tall, and with their distinctive yellow crown of feathers on their head, these birds are quite easy to recognize. They are mostly grey with a red inflatable throat pocket and white-streaked wings.

**Points: 25**

## SOUTHERN CASSOWARY

There are three species of cassowary but only the southern cassowary is found in Australia. Cassowaries are large and they can run at nearly 50 km/h (30 mph) and jump 1.5 m (5 feet) high.

## EMU

**Points: 10**

Emus are the second largest bird in the world and the biggest in Australia. They have two sets of eyelids, one set to keep out the dust and one set to blink with. Emus have light brown feathers with dark tips.

**Points: 10**

## OSTRICH

As it is the largest and heaviest bird in the world, it is not surprising that the ostrich is unable to fly. Instead, it is built for running very quickly to evade its predators. Females have brown and grey feathers while males are a bit more impressive with their striking black and white plumage.

## FLAMINGO

**Points: 5** 5

Most people will recognize a flamingo as soon as they see one. With their distinctive pink or reddish plumage, twig-like legs and hooked beaks, they are unlike any other bird. They get their red colour from the food they eat.

**Points: 5**

## PEACOCK

Their proper name is 'peafowl' and only the males are actually called peacocks. When on display, their multi-coloured tail feathers are simply stunning. All these feathers mean they can only fly short distances.

**Points: 20**

## EASTERN WHITE PELICAN

Also called the great white pelican, this is one of the largest flying birds in the world. They have large beaks which are pale orange on the underside. These beaks have a large pouch which they use to scoop up fish.

## SPOONBILL

**Points: 15**

These are tall waterbirds with long black legs and longs beaks with a flat end. Spoonbills feed with sideward sweeps of the head whilst wading in shallow water.

**Points: 20**

## TUFTED PUFFIN

These Pacific seabirds are similar in size to pigeons but are much heavier. They have orange webbed feet, black bodies, white faces, orange beaks and of course, a distinctive golden tuft, or plume, on their heads.

## EMPEROR PENGUIN

Points: 15

Emperor penguins are the largest of the penguin family and spend their whole life in Antarctica with its freezing waters. In mid-winter the males huddle together in large colonies to keep themselves, and the eggs they are looking after, warm.

 Points: 20

## KING PENGUIN

The second largest penguins in the world, these flightless birds are brilliant swimmers and live in and around the Southern Ocean. They have vivid orange and yellow patches on their necks, beaks and the sides of their heads.

## HUMBOLDT PENGUIN

Points: 15

Humboldt penguins live in large colonies along the coasts of Chile and Peru. In the water, they are amazingly well camouflaged. If you were to look up at them when they are swimming, you would see their white bellies mix in with sunshine. Looking down on them, their dark backs blend in with the water.

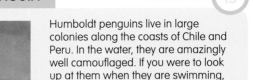

**Points: 20**

**ROCKHOPPER PENGUIN**

The rockhopper is one of the smallest penguins in the world. They are very distinctive due to their yellow and black feathers on the sides of their head. They get their name from the fact that they tend to live in rocky habitats and hop about rather than sliding on their bellies.

## EAGLE OWL

**Points: 15**

European eagle owls can have wingspans over 2 metres (6.5 feet) but it is their distinctive ear tufts that make them easy to spot.

**Points: 15**

## SNOWY OWL

Snowy owls breed in the Arctic tundra. They are very patient hunters and will wait on perches for long periods looking for their prey. Their acute hearing and superb eyesight helps them to do this.

## GREAT GREY OWL

**Points: 5**

One of the largest owls in the world by length, the great grey owl lives in coniferous forests in the northern hemisphere. They have large round heads and yellow eyes that have dark circles around them.

**Points: 10**

**KESTREL**

The kestrel is quite a small bird of prey and can be recognized by its reddish-brown plumage. Kestrels don't build their own nests and instead use old nests that other birds have left.

**WHITE-BACKED VULTURE**

**Points: 15**

This is the most common vulture in Africa. It never hunts and instead scavenges dead animals which it finds. It has a hooked black bill to tear off meat.

## RED-BELLIED PIRANHA

**Points: 25**

These fish from South America have a fearsome reputation. With their powerful jaws and razor-sharp teeth it is easy to see why. In large shoals they are capable of eating large animals in minutes. However, most of the time they just eat small fish, insects and sometimes plants.

**Points: 15**

It took a long time for scientists to decide that these creatures were actually fish. Despite looking like miniature hobby horses, they breathe through gills and control their buoyancy with a swim bladder – just like fish.

**CATFISH**

**Points: 10**

There are many species which make up the catfish family. They all appear to have something resembling cats' whiskers beside their mouths. These 'barbels', as they are called, have lots of taste buds on them to help catfish detect food.

**Points: 10**

**ELECTRIC EEL**

Electric eels aren't actually eels – they are more closely related to catfish and carp – but they can stun prey with a strong electrical charge. They use this to catch prey and to stop predators from eating them.

## SEA URCHIN

**Points: 10**

Sea urchins don't really look like animals at all as they don't have fins, eyes, claws or arms. Instead, they have lots of spines that protrude from their shells to protect them from predators. Sea urchins come in all sorts of colours.

**Points: 5**

## CORAL

These tiny organisms are best known for the large reefs they build over millions of years. One example is the Great Barrier Reef in Australia which is so big that it can be seen from space.

**Points: 20**

## MOUNTAIN CHICKEN FROG

One of the largest frogs in the world – they can weigh over 1 kg (2.2 pounds) – their meat tastes like chicken, hence their name. They can jump over a person because their legs are so powerful.

## GOLDEN DART FROG

**Points: 25**

South American tribesmen use the poison from these frogs on their arrows. They need to be careful though because the poison is strong enough to kill up to 20 people. So, these little frogs may look cute, but best to keep your distance.

### BLACK MAMBA

The black mamba is the fastest snake in the world and one of the deadliest. If they are threatened they become very aggressive and should be avoided at all times if you ever see one in the wild. Luckily for us, they don't live Europe.

Points: 20
double with answer

### KING COBRA

There are many different species of cobra snake but king cobras are the longest, reaching up to 5.5 metres (18 feet) in length. This makes them the longest venomous snakes in the world.

*What do they do if they are threatened?*

### BOA CONSTRICTOR

Points: 10

Like pythons, these snakes squeeze their prey until they can't breathe. They can grow to well over 3 metres (10 feet) long. They have saddle-like markings along their bodies and have small, hooked teeth. These help them to grab and hold prey.

**Points: 20**

## GREEN ANACONDA

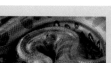

Female anacondas are much larger than males and can weigh up to 225 kg (550 pounds) and sometimes reach nearly 8.5 metres (28 feet) in length. These snakes are excellent swimmers and live in the swamps and marshes of South America.

## RETICULATED PYTHON

**Points: 30**

This is the largest species of python in the world and many have been known to grow to over 8 metres (26 feet). They are found in tropical rainforests, woodlands and nearby grasslands and are rarely far from water.

**Points: 20**

## DIAMONDBACK RATTLESNAKE

These venomous snakes from America have distinctive rows of diamond-shaped markings on their bodies. When threatened they will rattle their tales to warn off intruders. This rattling sound can be heard from quite far away.

## GREEN IGUANA

**Points: 15** 15

Although these large lizards are called 'green' iguanas, they can also be purple, orange and even blue in colour. Green iguanas have a third eye on top of their head. It's a bit different to their other eyes but it helps to alert them of approaching predators.

10 **Points: 10**

## CHAMELEON

These are part of the iguana family and have the ability to change colour depending on how they are feeling. They can do this quickly by adjusting special cells in their body.

*What other thing do all chameleons have in common?*

**Points: 10**

### BEARDED DRAGON

Bearded dragons are from Australia and get their name from their ability to puff out their throats to look like a beard. They often run on just their two back legs, instead of all four, to escape from predators in the wild.

### GILA MONSTER

**Points: 25**

Gila monsters are chunky lizards with pink or orange spots. They are native to the United States of America and one of the few venomous lizards in the world. As they have a very strong bite, they are not animals to step on by accident!

**Points: 15**

### RHINOCEROS IGUANA

Their name comes from the horn-like scales on their snouts that look similar to those on a rhino. The rough scales on their bodies can be olive-green, greyish-brown and sometimes black in colour. This helps to keep them well camouflaged.

## SUNDA GHARIAL

**Points: 40**   Top Spot!

These reptiles are also known as false gharials and are found in southeast Asia in freshwater environments. They have long slender snouts which help them catch fish.

 **Points: 20**

## CAIMAN

There are six different species of caiman in the swamps and rivers of Central and South America. They have rounded snouts unlike the more pointed v-shaped ones on crocodiles. Compared to alligators, they tend to be smaller in size and their teeth are more dagger-like.

## KOMODO DRAGON

**Points: 20**

These fearsome looking 'dragons' with long claws are the largest living lizards on Earth. They can reach 3 metres (10 feet) in length and their rough skin can be a mix of orange, green, grey and blue colours.

**Points: 15**

## BLACK WIDOW SPIDER

These are the most venomous spiders in North America and they eat many things including ants, beetles, scorpions and caterpillars. They are black all over with a red hour-glass shaped patch on their underside.

## SCORPION

**Points: 10**

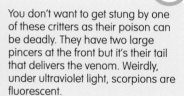

You don't want to get stung by one of these critters as their poison can be deadly. They have two large pincers at the front but it's their tail that delivers the venom. Weirdly, under ultraviolet light, scorpions are fluorescent.

**Points: 5**

## TARANTULA

Not many people want to get their hands on a tarantula. However, except for a painful bite, they are actually quite harmless to humans. In fact, a typical bee has stronger venom than this hairy spider.

## GIANT AFRICAN MILLIPEDE

**Points: 15**

There are 10,000 species of millipede and this one is the largest. They are black in colour and can grow to nearly 40 cm (15 inches) long. Despite their name they 'only' have a few hundred legs.

**Points: 15**

### ATLAS MOTH

The atlas moth has the largest wingspan of any moth in the world. It is a whopping 30 cm (12 inches) wide! Their name is thought to come from the lines and colours on their wings which resemble an atlas map.

### STICK INSECT

**Points: 5**

Across the world there are about 3,000 different species of stick insect, or phasmids, and they vary in size enormously. As their colour and shape mimic their surroundings, they can remain hidden for many hours waiting for prey.

**Points: 10**

## FEEDING TIME

Modern zoos will usually let visitors watch animals being fed or exercised. Events will be advertised around the zoo so you can plan ahead and make sure you don't miss it.

## MEET THE ANIMALS

**Points: 15**

Perhaps there is an opportunity to meet some of the animals. You might be able to feed them yourself or, if they are small enough, hold them in your hands. Remember to ask a zoo keeper first though.

### ZOO TRAIN

**Points: 10**

Many modern zoos have large enclosures for the animals so getting around can be hard work. Look out for zoo transport that will help you out. Score for any type of zoo transport you see.

**Points: 10**

### ACTIVITY TIME

Perhaps there is a play park with swings, slides and ropes. There might even be adventure parks or treetop walkways – if you've seen the monkeys you'll know what to do. Score if you take part in any activity.

### SOFT TOY

**Points: 5**

Most zoos will have a shop where you can buy books and pictures of animals. If you're lucky you might get a cuddly version of one of the creatures to take home.

# INDEX

**Answers: P7** They aren't sleepy. It's to display their amazingly large teeth to let the others know who is in charge **P11** They spend almost all their time in the trees. **P13** Most of their foraging is done at night. **P20** Porcupines can have more than 30,000 quills. **P22** Their teeth need to keep growing because they become ground down with all the chomping they do! **P28** They live in the Amazon river and in its tributaries. **P34** African elephants are bigger than Asian elephants and have larger ears that are a similar shape to the continent of Africa. **P54** They raise the front part of their bodies off the ground, flare their hoods and hiss. **P55** Very, very, long tongues.

# i-SPY

## How to get your i-SPY certificate and badge

Let us know when you've become a super-spotter with 1000 points and we'll send you a special certificate and badge!

## HERE'S WHAT TO DO!

- ✓ Ask an adult to check your score.

- ✓ Visit www.collins.co.uk/i-SPY to apply for your certificate. If you are under the age of 13 you will need a parent or guardian to do this.

- ✓ We'll send your certificate via email and you'll receive a brilliant badge through the post!